Arpad Haraszthy

Wine-Making in California

Arpad Haraszthy

With an Introduction by
Ruth Teiser and Catherine Harroun

THE BOOK CLUB OF CALIFORNIA
1978

©Copyright 1978
The Book Club of California
San Francisco, California

Publication Number 159

SIX HUNDRED COPIES
DESIGNED AND PRINTED BY LAWTON KENNEDY

Introduction

WINE-MAKING IN CALIFORNIA began about a century before the series of four articles by Arpad Haraszthy bearing that title appeared in *The Overland Monthly* of 1871 and 1872. The exact date the Franciscan fathers started making wine in California has not been ascertained, but it was within two or three years of their arrival in 1769 to establish the first of their Alta California missions. That they brought vines or cuttings of what we know as the Mission grape from Baja California has by now been established, but the place of origin of the variety remains in doubt. Current theory, however, favors one not mentioned by Arpad Haraszthy, an island off northern Africa.

The Mission grape is still widely planted in California, in spite of having been held in disfavor from the 1850's onward. Arpad Haraszthy's close colleague, Charles A. Wetmore, complained that wine made from it always gave him a headache and that its brandy drove him to the verge of suicide. It is still not recommended as a table wine grape. Contemporary views differ from Wetmore's and Haraszthy's only in holding it tolerable for making sweet wines.

A completely puzzling mystery, however, is another Mission grape that Arpad Haraszthy called the white Mission. No such variety has been found, either in California or in New Mexico, according to the leading expert on grape varieties in America, Dr. H. P. Olmo of the University of California at Davis. The idea of its existence may have arisen from the fact that white wine as well as red was made from what Arpad Haraszthy called the blue Mission, the single grape that in his day and ours has borne the Mission name.

In the century between the first wine-making in California and the publication of Arpad Haraszthy's articles, two major changes had occurred. In the early 1830's com-

1

mercial wine-making had begun, to supply California's still mainly Hispanic population. And in the 1850's, following increased demand by the polyglot goldrush settlers, came increased awareness of the need for scientific study. Much of the impetus for such study came from Colonel Agoston Haraszthy, father of Arpad, who preached the importance of experimenting in California with Europe's best grape varieties. In the year 1861, just a decade before the first of the *Overland Monthly* articles appeared, the state legislature authorized the Committee on the Improvement of the Grape Vine in California that Arpad Haraszthy described. Shortly thereafter, Agoston Haraszthy made his historic journey to Europe, visiting vineyards and authorizing the shipment of selected vines and cuttings to California. Arpad, then in France studying champagne making, accompanied his father on his tour.

Agoston Haraszthy, the most famous of nineteenth century California wine men, was a Hungarian aristocrat and army officer of remarkable energy and versatility. After political revolution ended his career in the Hungarian government, he went to Wisconsin where he became a land developer, entrepreneur, and agriculturist. There he tried unsuccessfully to grow grapes. In the last days of 1849 he and his family arrived in San Diego where he became sheriff, was elected state assemblyman, and again planted a vineyard. But there, although his vines grew, they did not produce grapes to his liking.

Moving to San Francisco in 1852, he planted imported vines close by Mission Dolores and south of the city near Crystal Springs. Not until he bought land in the Sonoma foothills, however, did he create a vineyard that satisfied him. It was the one his son described as the first large unirrigated vineyard in the state.

Arpad Haraszthy was the third of the six children of Agoston Haraszthy and the Polish noblewoman, Eleanora de Dedinsky Haraszthy. He was born in 1840 at his father's estate at Futtak in what was then southern Hungary, now northern Yugoslavia. He was taken to Wisconsin at the age of two and San Diego at the age of nine. His education was given careful attention. California schools of the 1850's not being considered adequate, he was taken east by his mother in 1851 and placed in academies first in New York, then in New Jersey. During vacations, with funds supplied by his father, he travelled widely in the Eastern United States and Canada.

Not until 1857 did he return to California. By then his family was established at Sonoma, where his father had bought acreage near that of General Mariano G. Vallejo and was starting his famed Buena Vista vineyards.

Arpad stayed at Sonoma only two months, however, before leaving for Paris to continue his education. For three years there he studied toward a career in civil engineering. Then his father persuaded him to change his goal. In 1860 he began the involvement with wine that would fill the remaining forty years of his life.

Carrying letters from the Master of the Household of Napoleon III, he left Paris for the Champagne district to begin his practical education in "the management of wines and the manufacture of Champagne," as his father desired. The Champagne house of De Venoge at Epernay agreed to give him instruction in exchange for "a very liberal sum." (The quotations are from a biographical memoir prepared by Hubert Howe Bancroft's history staff in 1886, a typescript corrected in Arpad Haraszthy's hand.)

At Epernay he remained for nearly two years, leaving however at intervals. For several months in the summer of

1861 he accompanied his father on his tour of vineyards and wineries in Switzerland, Germany, Italy and Spain.

Earlier that year he had begun sending articles on European viticulture to *The California Farmer,* the first of his many excellent writings on wine. From Paris that May he sent a report on the past year's vintage (poor), and concluded on a note that foretold the convictions about the California wine industry that he would carry throughout the coming years. He also indicated how thoroughly American he felt himself to be.

"In a few years, with enterprise and skillful management," he wrote, "we will show Europe that *we too* can make Wines, and that they only need care and age to make them renowned. It is just that Europe should supply Wine for her own use, but it is also just and not only just but *our duty* to supply Wine for the consumption of our Continent."

In 1862, when his training at Epernay was considered "complete" by both the cellarmaster and the proprietor of the house of De Venoge, he returned to California to participate in carrying out that duty.

At Sonoma, where his brothers Attila and Gaza had also established vineyards, Arpad was put in charge of his father's cellar and made the wine from the 1862 harvest. The next year was even more eventful for the young man. He produced his first champagne, and he was married. On June 1 he and his brother Attila married daughters of their neighbor, General Vallejo. Arpad's wife, Jovita, was considered the beauty of the Vallejo family.

Colonel Haraszthy, encouraged by his son's first experiments with champagne, directed him to make more the following year. Of the "nine or ten thousand bottles" he produced, however, none was successful. He believed he knew the cause of the failure and how to prevent it from occurring again. But meantime his father had organized the Buena Vista Vinicultural Society, a corporation, with the participation of a number of California wine dealers and the backing of the powerful William C. Ralston. It was said to be Ralston who refused to sanction Arpad's further champagne making. The young man resigned from the organization and formed a wholesale wine firm in Sonoma with a partner. He could hardly have found enough challenge in that, however, and in planting a few small vineyards for others and one for himself in the hills nearby. When in 1866 Isidor Landsberger, a director of the Buena Vista Vinicultural Society, asked him to join him in his San Francisco wine business, Arpad readily accepted. He and his wife and their two-year-old daughter Agostine left the home he had built which Jovita described as "a little shanty up in the ravine, a beautiful spot," and moved to the city.

In San Francisco Arpad continued his experiments with champagne. Madie Brown Emperan described, in *The Vallejos of California,* how he and Jovita, in the parlor of their San Francisco home, developed the champagne which he named Eclipse after a then popular cigar. The former is probably an oversimplification, the latter a misapprehension. Both the cigar and the champagne were undoubtedly named for the celebrated eighteenth century English race horse, Eclipse. Be that as it may, the 1867 San Francisco city directory lists Arpad Haraszthy as "champagnemaker with I. Landsberger," and in that year regular production of Eclipse began. It was California's first commercially successful champagne. Landsberger showed faith in it by relinquishing his agency for products of the Buena Vista Vinicultural Society, which was continuing its attempts to produce champagne.

By 1871, when the *Overland Monthly* articles on wine-making began appearing, Arpad Haraszthy had seen his champagne well launched, and he was now a partner in I. Landsberger & Co. He was also taking a place in the social life of the city. He was, according to descriptions, a tall, well proportioned convivial boulevardier, a man who enjoyed fine wines, fine foods, good company and good conversation. In the spring of 1872 he became a charter member of the Bohemian Club. At the time of his death the editor of the *Pacific Wine and Spirits Review* described him as "a true gentleman, thoroughly educated, a linguist, a wit, and a most entertaining conversationalist — above all a Bohemian in the fullest sense of the word."

The Bohemian Club was originally an organization of "journalists and other writers, artists, actors and musicians." Arpad Haraszthy undoubtedly qualified for membership as a journalist, for he never ceased writing about grapes and wine. Another charter member was Charles A. Wetmore, then a reporter on the *Alta California,* later an associate of Haraszthy.

The address of I. Landsberger & Co. was first 429 Jackson Street, then 423-429, then 10-12 Jones Alley. The business in both still wines and champagne was growing, and its premises were expanding both above and below ground. Jones Alley, now Hotaling Place, ran along the side of the Jackson Street building. Part of the complex still stands. Early in April of 1871, to display its expanded quarters, the firm held an open house. Between five and six hundred of its "patrons and invited guests" were served a "bountiful lunch" according to an enthusiastic report in the San Francisco *Morning Call.* Landsberger and Haraszthy spoke to them of the benefits of California champagne production not only to the state's grape growers and skilled laborers, but also to its "box manufacturers, foil-beaters, label-

RIESLING

ORLEANS VINEYARD

ARPAD HARASZTHY & CO.

SAN FRANCISCO, CAL.

printers, cork-merchants, bottle-makers and wire manufacturers."

Nevertheless, they made no elaborate claims for their champagne. In a printed circular given the guests, they traced the history of champagne making in California back to 1856, well before Arpad Haraszthy's experiments began, and the *Call* noted, "While they do not profess that their champagnes as yet equal the best imported sparkling wines, they claim that they are entitled to encouragement for the efforts they are making to produce as good an article as the best, and that they will be enabled in a few years to compete with the popular imported varieties."

Similarly, in the *Overland Monthly* articles that began appearing later that year, Arpad Haraszthy made no mention of California champagne. It is indicative of his balanced view of the California wine industry that he did not give notice to so small a segment of it, in spite of the fact that it was a segment in which he was intensely involved.

There has been speculation that the reason Arpad Haraszthy's first champagne failed was that it was made from Mission grapes. That seems unlikely. Nevertheless, we do know that by 1883 the grapes he was using were "mainly Riesling, Berger, Gutadel, Muscatel and Zinfandel...chosen for their color, lightness of body, saccharine properties and alcoholic strength"—this according to a pamphlet he deposited in Hubert Howe Bancroft's library. It has not been learned if he experimented with the traditional French champagne grapes, Pinot noir, Chardonnay and Pinot Meunier.

As Arpad became increasingly absorbed in his business and the larger affairs of the state's wine industry, difficulties arose in his relationship with his wife Jovita. Stable as he was in his occupation, indications are that he was not a domestic sort of man. Nor apparently was he making much money. They had no servant. Their first home Jovita had characterized as "a little shanty." What their San Francisco homes were like is not known, but there were seven different ones in the twelve years before Jovita's death in 1878. At least some provided room for guests, for family-loving Jovita often had one or another of the Vallejo women staying with her. But in the early spring of 1877, when General Vallejo, deeply troubled, went to San Francisco to try to dissuade his daughter from divorcing her husband, he stayed, uncomfortably, at the Commercial Hotel.

By the time he arrived, husband and wife were communicating only in writing. Jovita had gone to a lawyer to initiate divorce proceedings.

"Arpad wants me to manage the case," the General wrote to his wife, "because I will look after the interest and honor of Jovita, of her children, and also the interests of the Haraszthy family. I could wish with all my heart to avoid a scandal and to placate Jovita a little, but she is determined in everything."

She continued determined, in spite of her husband having written "several letters asking her pardon."

"With feelings of kindness," he wrote in one, "I address you this time and ask you once again to forget the past and return to me as my wife. I am not only willing but even anxious to acknowledge to you, all those errors I have committed.... And I hope, Jovita, you will pardon them. I must own that my nature is hasty and impetuous and I get angry easily." He had made a similar admission to Colonel J. L. L. Warren of the *California Farmer,* his first editor, twenty-six years earlier.

Finally General Vallejo was able to write to his wife, "Jovita gives in (not because she wants to) only for the sake of the children. This week I expect to finish the *cure* and will go home to rest...." As his departure neared he could report, "The sea that has been so stirred up has subsided; it is serene and peaceful."

The following May, however, having given birth to a child who died shortly after, Jovita herself suddenly died. To Arpad was left the rearing of their two children as well as his private and public wine industry activities. Family members sometimes came to help him, and he maintained a close relationship with the Vallejos, always loyal to and respectful of the General, and employing Jovita's brother Napoleon as a salesman. His domestic instability appeared to change only slightly, however, for in the twenty-two years between his wife's death and his own, he had nine different San Francisco addresses.

His business premises remained, however, those that he had occupied since his arrival in San Francisco in 1866. When in 1879 I. Landsberger & Co. sold its good will to Arpad Haraszthy & Co., the successor firm continued at the same stand. Now the "and Co." was Henry Epstein, whose father had at one time had an interest in the Landsberger firm and who himself had had a solid career as a legislator and rancher in Nevada and a businessman in California. It was undoubtedly he who furnished most of the capital and probably much of the business management of the firm and of the Orleans vineyard and winery in Yolo County which it acquired in 1881.

Meanwhile, Arpad Haraszthy had become increasingly active in affairs affecting all of California's vintners. In the mid-1870's he had promulgated and led the campaign for federal legislation that would alleviate the problems of brandy production that he described in the *Overland Monthly*. In 1878 he was elected president of the State

Vinicultural Society and led its campaign for tariff protection against French wines. He continued to head the organization until 1886.

In 1880 Eugene W. Hilgard, the Professor of Agriculture at the University of California, and Haraszthy appeared before the state legislature to urge the creation of a Board of State Viticultural Commissioners. It was to promote California viticulture in general, and in particular to rally forces to fight the phylloxera. This was the root louse that by then had devastated many of Europe's finest vineyards and, in spite of Haraszthy's earlier assertion that California conditions had a purifying effect upon imported vines, was infecting an increasing number of plantings in this state. The Board was intended to supplement the scientific work to be done under Professor Hilgard at the University, for which a separate appropriation was asked. Both requests were approved. The governor appointed nine of the state's leading wine men as commissioners; Arpad Haraszthy was one, and he became its president. It was a position he continued to hold for the next eight years. Charles A. Wetmore, who was by now active in the wine industry and had, at Arpad Haraszthy's urging, been sent to France to report upon wines and the phylloxera there, became the Board's chief executive officer.

The Board promoted California wines, held meetings at which wine makers exchanged data and judged each other's bottlings, published papers, and provided information to the vineyardists. A rift developed, however, between the Board and the University, especially between Charles A. Wetmore and Professor Hilgard, because the wine man feared the phylloxera might be carried from the University's experimental plot to the commercial vineyards. Arpad Haraszthy, caught between them, sided strongly with Wetmore. Eventually the matter was settled with the gradual general acceptance of the theory that grafting wine varieties onto phylloxera-resistant American grape vine rootstock was the way to withstand the pest. By then, though, the rift was too broad to be bridged.

Details of the discord are found in correspondence between Hilgard and Haraszthy and in newspaper reports, but no clear record exists why Arpad Haraszthy was removed from the Board in 1888. Some politics were involved, but whether or not Professor Hilgard played a part is impossible to determine. In any case, Governor R. W. Waterman refused to reappoint Haraszthy when his second term ended, in spite of strong protest from many members of the wine industry.

Arpad Haraszthy responded as he might have been expected to, in a way that benefitted the industry and its subsequent historians as well. He prepared a detailed review of the work of the Board through its first eight years. His report included general statistics and broad recommendations for the industry's advancement on many fronts, from enlarging markets to reducing freight rates. Yet, humanly enough, he ended his letter of transmittal to the Governor with the statement that he felt so full a report to be necessary because *"in certain quarters* there exists, apparently, *a determined ignorance* regarding the work accomplished by this Commission, as well as a *sustained endeavor* to cloud the actual value of its labors."

It was an unfortunate and, in the perspective of history, unnecessary rift. Haraszthy joined Wetmore, Isaac De Turk, and other Hilgard opponents in attempting to establish a separate college of viticulture, but the University went on under Hilgard's guidance and that of his successors to become one of the world's great institutions of viticultural done, for it did not require a great quantity.

Members of the Board of State Viticultural Commissioners worked constantly but received no pay, so it was undoubtedly fortunate that Henry Epstein continued a partner in Arpad Haraszthy & Co. The firm weathered the general economic depression of the mid-1870's, and continued the Orleans vineyard plantings of varieties that Arpad Haraszthy considered best suited to the area. In 1883 he had 140 acres of Riesling and Zinfandel in full bearing, and that same year, at the second annual meeting of the state's wine men sponsored by the Viticultural Board, he not only gave papers on wine grape varieties, fermentation and care of new wines, he also showed "a common claret" probably made from Orleans Zinfandels. By 1888 he had increased the Orleans plantings. That year he entered fourteen of its wines in the "Instructive Exhibit" at the viticultural convention. They included "Pinot rose," (a red wine, not a rosé), Orleans Riesling, Zinfandel, and such later-to-be forgotten varietals as Tannat and Boal.

By that year California's vineyards and wineries were, however, in economic trouble. A market crisis had begun in 1886 with a very large but poor crop of grapes, and hard times continued into the 1890's. As a result several wine companies organized the California Wine Association to stabilize markets and prices. In 1894 seven of the state's leading wine merchants agreed to put their holdings into this joint corporation. Although Arpad Haraszthy & Co. was the smallest of them, Henry Epstein, who went on the board to represent the firm, was elected chairman.

It was an uneasy alliance for Arpad Haraszthy himself. His struggle to maintain independence is reflected in the water-blurred script of the Association's first minute book. He wanted to continue at least supervision of the making of Eclipse champagne by himself or by his son Carlos who had recently joined him. There were proposals and counterproposals. In the end the Orleans winery and land immediately surrounding it were made over in return for stock in the Association, while Arpad Haraszthy bought back the champagne making equipment and part of the inventory at the San Francisco headquarters that had previously been transferred to the Association. Henry Epstein departed from the Haraszthy firm and the Association. Thereafter Arpad Haraszthy listed himself as simply "vine grower and producer Haraszthy champagnes." His son left. He retained only part of the former company premises.

The last five years of his life were not prosperous. In 1896 the Orleans vineyard was sold, but the proceeds from his equity in it were apparently not sufficient to make him comfortable. His champagne boom, such as it had been, was over. In the spring of 1900 he went to Alaska with a younger brother, Bela, a miner, to locate claims they hoped would be profitable. Early in November he returned, having been ill and so far unsuccessful, but he was determined to continue the pursuit the next spring. Meanwhile his daughter, the widowed Mrs. George D. Strickland, had been keeping the business going. She had been a photographer in New York, and she had installed her photographic equipment in a rear office room.

Around midnight on November 16th, 1900, waiting for a cable car to take him home from an evening visit, Arpad Haraszthy collapsed on the sidewalk at the corner of Hyde and Washington streets. A special police officer and a medical student who were on the car he was awaiting rushed to his aid and called an ambulance, but he died before he reached the hospital.

The newspapers attempted to call up a romance between the sixty-year-old Haraszthy and a young secretary who had worked in his office, and one account stated that he was said to have a back room in his place of business where he photographed young ladies while generously pouring champagne.

Generous indeed he was with his champagne, having furnished it to many a gathering, private and public. But he had been for nearly forty years yet more generous with his time and effort and devotion to California's wine industry. It was his friend Charles A. Wetmore who characterized him best. A decade before Arpad Haraszthy's death, Wetmore wrote of his "gentle encouragement" and "friendly helpfulness" to his fellow-vintners. "His courage and unwavering hopefulness have given us all strength, and his unspotted integrity, his cheerful candor, his constant breathing of aspirations for ideals of perfection have given us a central figure on which to rally and maintain our *esprit de corps.*"

It is these qualities that are reflected in the series of articles Arpad Haraszthy wrote for *The Overland Monthly*. They are candid, hopeful, aspiring to perfection for winemaking in California. A number of his recommendations were achieved with the later passage of pure food and labelling laws and various tax concessions. Just as history is constantly being revised, so are practices and theories of grape growing and wine making. A number of the practices Arpad Haraszthy described have changed with time, and a century more of experience has made us less sanguine about the patterns of both weather and the economy of the industry. Yet there are few theories given in these articles written in 1871 that wine men of the last quarter of the twentieth century would completely reject. Some they would debate, but the majority of Arpad Haraszthy's ideas remain valid.

Ruth Teiser
Catherine Harroun

PART ONE

Almost every wine-growing country in the Old World owes its first plantation of vines to the monks; and such was their knowledge of soil and locality, that the result of their labors has gained a reputation that has outlived them hundreds of years. To their labors alone are we indebted for the wines of Johannisberg, Steinberg, Hockheim, Romané Conti, Clos-Vougeot, l'Hospice, Chambertin, Château Yquem, Margaux, Laffitte, St. Julien, and many others. To them are we even indebted for the bright, sparkling, and ever-lively champagne, that warms without intoxication, and makes languid conversation bubble with the spirit of wit, like its own vivacious self. And what the monks did for the Old World, that did the Fathers for California. They planted the first vine, and they made our first wine.

About the year 1771, the vine was first known to be planted in our State, and the Mission San Gabriel claims the honor of possessing the first vineyard. The early history of this vineyard, as well as the origin of its vines, is lost in the past, but has given rise to many speculations. It is believed by some that the vines were brought, by roots or cuttings, from Spain, either directly or by way of Mexico; others hold that these vines were taken from some one of the many wild varieties that are scattered over the whole State; and there is still another theory, which is upheld by General M. G. Vallejo, than whom there is no better authority on the subject in the state. According to his statement, the Fathers first tried to make wine from the wild grapes, but, being unsuccessful, planted the seeds from raisins that came from Spain. The result of these experiments gave them several varieties, among which are our present blue Mission and a white grape of a musky flavor. These two, after due trial, they retained and propagated, rejecting all the others.

The first two theories are certainly very defective; for, even with the quick and certain journey that can be made in our days of steam locomotion, an enormous percentage of roots and cuttings die on the trip—in fact, but a very small percentage reach us in a living condition, and it requires all the advanced horticultural skill of our age to revive and sustain them. As for once being of the wild species, they do not bear the faintest resemblance, either in fruit, leaf, or wood, to any wild variety. The bunches and grapes are large, the leaf full and decidedly marked, and the joints comparatively close, while their branches are sturdy—characteristics that are seldom found singly, and never collectively, in any one wild species of grape-vine.

More probable than either of these theories, is that the seeds were purposely sent out from Spain, through Government authority, as certainly were the orange, the lime, the olive, the fig, etc. And this is the only rational manner of explaining the presence of the same two varieties—blue and white so-called Mission grape—in New Mexico, where they are universally cultivated. The missions in both provinces, being under the direction of the same power in Spain, would naturally receive the same selections of seeds. It is claimed by experts that the blue Mission grape is the same as the Beni-Carlo, but that does not alter the strength of the argument, for it may be its seedling, just as the Pineau [Pinot noir] of Burgundy has some eighty different seedlings, each and every one closely resembling the parent grape and vine.

It matters little, however, practically, where the first vines came from. They were known to grow at the Mission San Gabriel, and from there the planting of the blue Mission was extended from mission to mission, until not a single one was without it. The blue grape seems to have been the favorite with the Fathers, and undoubtedly because its wine resembled the red wines of Old Castile.

It is possible, that, while the vineyards were small, their products were used at table, and not much wine made from them, but this limitation could not have lasted for a longer period than the conclusive proof of the prolific qualities of the vine. And thus we have traditions handed down to us, that those missions, having a greater number of vines, made very considerable quantities of wine. There were few, if any, missions that, at the time of the arrival of the Americans, did not have at least five acres, and many had fifteen, twenty, and even thirty acres of vineyard. As the greatest care and attention was bestowed upon these vines—as labor was no object, and they were all planted in rich soil and irrigated—they certainly could not have produced less than from seven hundred to one thousand gallons of wine per acre, even withholding what grapes may have been used at table.

These wines, it is likely, were all used in the neighborhood, as there were no facilities for export, there being neither bottles nor casks to put the wine in, nor any regular communication with other countries. Indeed, the making of these wines was crude in the extreme; they were fermented in cemented cisterns, and then either left there or drawn into sewed-up hides, or placed in stationary earthenware jars of great size. Here they remained, without further care or attention, until consumed, and they were not likely to attain any great age or good quality from such handling. Neither did any of the missions achieve any reputation for the excellence of their wines, though it is said that there was some preference given to the wine from the Sonoma Mission, which was probably owing more to the fine quality of the soil than to superior skill in handling.

Owing, then, to a want of care, knowledge, and the necessary appliances, it is more than probable that these wines never attained any age, but must have been consumed during the twelve months following their manufacture. One strong reason for this belief is the fact that the old Californians of those days had a great partiality for sweet wines, and used every known means to prolong the excessive sweetness of their new wines; and to attain this end, they boiled the juice, and even added brandy to it. As one of the products of these efforts, we have the Angelica wine, whose mode of manufacture may not have originated in California, but certainly was universally adopted by the Spanish-American inhabitants, who are, to this day, very fond of this grape *liqueur,* for a wine it certainly can not correctly be called. All wines gradually lose their natural sweetness as they attain age, and this rule holds good even with those that have been brandied; therefore, it is quite probable that all these wines were consumed and disposed of by the Fathers before the period came when their sweet taste was gone.

Raisins were also made at these missions for home use, the Fathers possessing both the patience and the knowledge required to make them; but owing to the grapes from which they were made, they could neither have been of a fair size nor of fine flavor, though quite good for cooking purposes, and even passable for the table, where no others were to be found.

A kind of brandy was also manufactured by the Fathers, which must have been as crude as their wine, and was mostly used to fortify it.

There seemed to be nothing that grew, or could be grown, that the civilizing enterprise of the Fathers did not attempt to produce. Gathering in the milder disposed Indians of the neighborhood, they taught them the tillage of the soil, and made artisans of them. Nature smiled upon their efforts—all that they planted grew, while for a time peace and prosperity surrounded them. Their humble churches gradually grew into splendor; high walls protected their orchards and vineyards from profane trespassers; their granaries were full, and their wine-vaults overflowing. Nothing more was necessary to fill their cup of happiness, and it must have been a proud moment to them, indeed, as they sat quietly under the vine and fig-tree, and saw that all their years of toil had been crowned with success. And the sight of one of these missions, in the height of its prosperity—with its broad acres of grain, filled with busy toilers, its fine churches, the numerous towers and walls, the vineyards, the orange and olive-groves—must have been a pleasant one, indeed.

But this vision of peace and plenty was not destined to last long. The outside world became suspicious and jealous of the influence and wealth of the Fathers, nor ceased their workings until they had despoiled the missions of their lands and the Fathers of the result of their labors. And when the Americans came into possession of the territory, they found most of the missions in ruins, their orchards and vineyards neglected, while the old Indian cultivators were scattered far and wide.

Yet, to some far-seeing minds, the too evident past thrift, and even present vigor, of the neglected stumps, foreshadowed what might be done in the future, with proper care and training. Some few of these people, not diverted by the gold-fever, settled upon or near these missions, and redeemed, replanted, and extended the cultivation of the vine in a small way. Owing, however, to the lack of facilities in transportation, the vineyards remained very limited in extent, and their products were mostly used at table, or were worked up into a harsh brandy, poor in quality, which was generally disposed of to the Indians. Only enough wine was made to supply the local demand, and that was easily education and research.

In the years 1852 and 1853, grapes were selling in and around Los Angeles, on the vines, from two to six cents per pound, and, though they brought in San Francisco from fifty cents to one dollar per pound, there had been no one with sufficient time to supply the demand. The late Colonel [Agoston] Haraszthy was the first to turn his attention to this business on a large scale. He bought up whole crops of grapes from the different small vineyards during those two seasons, and forwarded them to San Francisco, realizing therefrom what was called a handsome profit, even in those flush times. The door once open, there was no longer any scarcity, and, every season following, the supply became more abundant.

In 1855, Charles Kohler and Mr. [John] Frohling established a native-wine house in San Francisco, the former intending to dispose of the wines in the city, while his partner was to manufacture them in Los Angeles. Neither of these gentlemen was experienced in the undertaking, and the wines they offered for sale were not clear, but rough, new, and crude, and, notwithstanding their guaranteed purity, found very slow sale. But, despite all these drawbacks, the firm struggled on in the hazardous enterprise, and became finally successful in creating three or four opposition houses. It was at about this period that a few masterly spirits persisted in bringing before the public, by numerous newspaper items, the certainty of realizing large profits from the cultivation of the grape. We have before us one of these items, that appeared in the columns of our local press, and, to give the reader some idea how calculations were made in those early days, we present the following liberal, but literal, extracts:

"*Editors Alta:*—Your able article concerning the culture of grapes and the production of wine, seemed to me a kind of challenge for every citizen to contribute his mite: First, to promote every kind of industry beneficial to our Golden State; second, to substitute for unwholesome beverages, as brandy, whisky, gin, etc., a natural, unadulterated drink; third, to retain as much as possible of California gold among ourselves, that goes now for said article to foreign countries; fourth, to thus bring land into cultivation that would yet for many a year remain unimproved; fifth, to create a new branch of industry and home commerce, the most advantageous for the community at large; sixth, to give employment to men of different trades, as vine-dressers, coopers, wine-dealers, iron-mongers, timber-mer- etc.: and, seventh, to give men of sound judg-

advantages and humbug—
profitable manner,
while it will never
ly on *luck* and *cir-*

tself, but of little
on of the writer's
the plan of 19,900
s from distance to

n thriving, 160 acres

	Brandy, galls.	Almonds, lbs.
s.		
)0	50	. . . . .
)0	300	. . . . .
00	2,000	10,000
)00	3,500	25,000
Sixth year)00	5,000	60,000
Total 216,000	10,800	95,000

Taking the wine at only $1 the gallon, brandy at $2, almonds one shilling a pound, would make the aggregate returns $249,475

The expenditure for preparing the land and planting, as by estimate No. 1 $7,600
The expenditure for cultivation, barrels, transportation, and exchange, estimate No. 2   71,300
                                                   78,900
     Would leave a clear gain of $170,575

"And while $15,000 would amply cover all, up to the time the first
returns could be expected to defray expenses, this enterprise would
pay, during the first six years, a complete percentage of $1,193.16; or,
per annum, $198.86 for each $100 invested — equal to $16.57 per
month. I challenge any business man in California to show, in any
enterprise, such high figures, without possible failure for years. Add
to this, that the production by this system will yearly increase considerably; . . . . so, for instance, in the second term of six years, the
total yield would be: wine, about 800,000 gallons; brandy, 40,000
gallons; almonds, 500,000 pounds."

This item was written with the best of faith, and, although it brought forth no direct takers in its proposed
enterprise, it produced, in conjunction with preceding and
subsequent articles upon the same topic, more general inquiry concerning this new pursuit. After mature reflection,
this was considered almost as good as stumbling over lumps
of gold, and many people began to plant a few acres of
vines — just a few acres, because, at such rates, a few acres
would be enough. Many who planted certainly believed
that all their grapes could be disposed of for table use; but,
even should they be forced to make wine at $2 per gallon,
a thousand gallons per acre would realize for them the
profitable sum of $2,000 per acre—a very handsome income
from so small an investment. There arose only one doubt
in their minds — and that was, prices might fall in consequence of overproduction; but this was set at rest by the
fact, that, even at one-half the above price, it would pay
well, and many people took the risk.

The method followed, in the setting out of these new

vineyards, was the same as that which the Fathers had adopted; the vines were the same species; the location and soil were always chosen as nearly the same as possible — locating the vines where they could be irrigated, and choosing a rich, heavy soil. Irrigation was considered indispensable, both for the growth of the vines and the production of fruit; and it was a long-believed maxim that nothing would grow in California without irrigation.

It was in the winter of the year 1858, that the first large vineyard was planted in a locality where irrigation could not possibly be undertaken. This vineyard consisted of 140 acres, or about eighty thousand vines, and was planted by Colonel Agoston Haraszthy. Many were the prophecies with reference to this plantation, which, in the mildest terms, was considered a rash and dangerous experiment. It was closely watched by all interested in the pursuit, and it can be safely said, that upon its success depended the future magnitude of the wine interest of the State; not as to what it is to-day, but as to what it will surely be fifty years hence.

Up to the year 1858, Los Angeles County possessed fully one-half of all the vines in the State, and, without a doubt, would have continued to hold that proportion, had those few acres of unirrigated vines failed. But they did not fail, contrary to all the prophecies of old and experienced residents. They outlived the dry season, and, in due time, bore a fine crop of grapes, whose wine was immediately pronounced as having a finer, freer taste, and richer flavor, than that made from irrigated vines. These results soon came to be known, and a new era began in the vine-culture of California. Hundreds of acres of hill-side lands were taken up and planted with vines, until there was hardly a county in the whole State that did not have its vineyard planted, where no water could reach it, but that falling from the clouds, or shed by the soft dew of the heavens.

It was also about this period that a more concentrated attention was drawn to the varieties of grape that should be planted in the future. Several years previous, a number of varieties had been secured and brought to the State, by a few enterprising persons; but their selections had been made, almost exclusively, for consumption as table-grapes. However, these private collections, which were brought from Europe, as well as from the Patent Office at Washington, had been planted long enough to demonstrate conclusively, that, in each particular case, they would thrive here, bear well, and produce a fruit in many respects superior, for table use, to the favorite blue Mission grape. From this, it was presumed that the same improvement would occur in the wines that were produced from choicer varieties of grapes. There were then but few people in California who had been engaged practically as wine-producers in Europe, and even these few had their attention turned to other pursuits; but enough were found of partial European experience to testify that, in the Old World, more stress was laid upon the species of the grape, generally, than upon any other conditions.

Curiosity and enterprise becoming active, experiments were instituted on a more general plan throughout the State. Still, the extent to which these experiments were carried was much too limited, compared to the interest involved; but there was no immediate remedy, for there were but few attainable varieties, and even none of these were known as wine-grapes in Europe. Each vintage illustrated in a plainer manner the necessity of such, and even greater, experiments; for, although a good common wine had been produced by the Mission grape — a wine that pleased those who had not acquired a taste for European wines—still, it found little or no favor among connoisseurs and habitual wine-drinkers, for they pronounced our wines either fiery and earthy, or sweet and insipid. Nor was their judgment far from the truth, those wines produced by irrigated vines being generally both fiery and earthy, while those made from non-irrigated vines were apt to be of too much body, and too sweet in taste, when made from the blue Mission grape. It was true, that the sweetness of the latter wines would disappear by age; but, nevertheless, they did not acquire, even by long keeping, that inviting bouquet, so apparent in most of the good class of European wines, and so invariably sought after by all lovers of wine.

This bouquet quality, then, it was supposed, and partly proved, would never be acquired, in sufficient quantity, by a wine made from the Mission grape, be it planted in any soil, or whatever locality. Time and experiments have since completely proved the correctness of this supposition; and nothing is more positive, than that *the species of the grape gives the quality to the wine, and the soil only modifies that quality.*

In 1861, the State Legislature, perceiving the importance of the vinicultural interest, appointed a "Commission upon the Ways and Means best adapted to promote the Improvement and Growth of the Grape-vine in California." This Commission consisted of Colonel [John J.] Warner, Mr. [Theodore L.?] Schell, and Colonel Haraszthy. Colonel Warner made a very able report upon the grape interest, as he then found it, with many valuable suggestions, while Mr. Schell visited, and made an interesting report upon the viniculture of, the South American States. Colonel Haraszthy, finding that the vines imported by various private persons, as well as himself, were too costly, inadequate, and often unreliable, determined to visit each of the different wine-producing countries of Europe, and make personal selections, in his official capacity, of all the different varieties of grape-vines that he could collect. The result of his labors was an ample report made to the Legislature, and the importation of nearly two hundred thousand rooted vines and cuttings, which embraced in the neighborhood of three hundred distinct varieties, though they came catalogued under four hundred and ninety-two different names.

These different varieties of grape-vines were dispersed throughout the State, and planted in many varied localities. From practical results, some have been found far superior to others; but not a single variety in this vast collection has not done well, and raised and matured its fruit to perfection.

Upon the first arrival of these vines, but few vine-growers were willing to hazard the planting of any single variety in considerable quantity. They generally planted a few hundred vines, choosing a dozen or more of the different kinds. Sufficient quantities were, however, thus set out to give the most favorable and decided results upon this all-important question. And at present, there are very considerable quantities of wine made from such fine varieties of the grape as the Riesling, White Frontignan, Pineau or Burgundy grape, Traminer, Black Malvoisia, Zinfandel, and many others. These varieties of grape-vines, in every case, have not only been found to produce a finer wine than the Mission grape, but, also, when properly trained and pruned, to yield a greater crop to the acre. They possess still another advantage — and that is, a much greater uniformity from year to year in their bearing qualities.

There are those who are ever prone to prophesy evil, and so it was with regard to these varieties of wine-grapes.

It was said that they would die out, that after a few years they would change their qualities and degenerate, and that they would not reproduce a shadow of the qualities they gave in Europe. Time and facts have given these assertions the most emphatic denial; and it has been conclusively proved, that the character of the grape has not changed in fifteen years of cultivation in our State.

As has been already mentioned, the type of the grape governs the peculiar type of its product, the wine; therefore, though a wine made from the Riesling grape, grown in our State, may not resemble in every minute particular a wine made from the same variety grown in Germany, and be its exact counterpart, nevertheless the type of the two wines will be identical, and an experienced German wine-maker would most surely recognize our wine as one made from the Riesling grape, all other things being equal. This assertion has been tested and verified, in very many cases, with several of the finer imported varieties, and the result has invariably been the same in each separate case.

The climate and soil certainly have a marked influence upon the immediate quality of the grape, but not on its type, which it would take ages to change. Experience has shown us that the black Pineau, in our State, makes a sweeter, heavier, and fuller-bodied wine than in the Côte d'Or; but no one conversant with these matters will pronounce our wine from that grape other than a full-fledged Burgundy wine: the bouquet is there, and the whole type is there.

The very fact that the wine manufactured from each variety of grape has invariably made a distinct quality of wine, preserving its own peculiar taste and character, has almost resulted in a disadvantage to the vintner, for he is now at a loss to know which grape he shall set out, and which reject, for they all grow and all seem to make good wines. Time and experience alone can settle this difficulty, though it might be sooner brought about by first deciding whether the land which is to be planted resembles in quality that of any certain spot in the Old World, and whether the mean temperatures throughout the year, in the two spots, are nearly alike; and, if so, plant with the identical species of vine that the European vineyard was planted with. Then, if the mode of manufacture be conducted in the same manner, a wine will be made resembling in type and all its general characteristics that produced in the European vineyard.

This is the only rational mode of proceeding, and the surest road to a quick result. Thus, there can undoubtedly be produced wines resembling closely in type Sherry, Port, Madeira, Claret, Burgundy, and Hock.

But, heretofore, owing partly to the want of different varieties of grapes, but mostly to ignorance, which, in its self-confidence, overstepped the line of possibility, and counted too much upon art, most of our wine-makers were led into the delusive idea that skill in the mode of manufacture gave the wine its peculiar type, and they, until within the past few years, continued to attempt to manufacture all the types known by simply changing the details of manufacture. They attempted to reproduce every distinctive quality of wine in the world with the Mission grape.

The next great and very serious error that the vintners fell into, was that all the qualities came from the soil alone, and the Mission grape was planted in an endless variety of soil. True, in some, with certain exposures, the wine was much better than in others; but still the bouquet was not there, nor did the wine resemble any of those finer and numerous varieties of favorite European wines. Too much importance had been given the soil, and none at all to the character of the grape, which alone creates the type of the wine. They were lead into the erroneous belief that any grape, on a certain soil, would produce a superior wine, from remarking that different localities in the Old World, planted with the same variety of vine, even in the same climate—in fact, actually adjacent to each other—produced a quality which varied abruptly from indifferently good to the finest wine in the world. Unfortunately, they did not consider the result of planting an inferior species of grape in the soil that produced the fine wine: the result is known beyond peradventure. The product from such a grape, though it does acquire some degree of quality from the soil, never has been found equal to that produced from the superior variety on the same soil, nor even equal to those planted on a less favored soil with the superior grape.

Happily for the future reputation of the California wines, the false conclusions above alluded to are fast losing ground, and the results of experiments actually taking place show more and more that there is an unfailing adaptability of certain varieties of vines to certain soils, and that when these two conditions are filled, the highest possible excellence is attained by that particular variety of grape.

The best result has followed the experiments, by individual producers, to make from a single vineyard, and one species of grape, all the known kinds of wine. This benefit came in a negative manner, and demonstrated conclusively the non-adaptability of particular vineyards, and even whole districts, to produce certain classes of wines. Each district is gradually confining itself to its own proper character of wine, and a few years hence it will be known to a certainty which district is best adapted for producing a certain class of wine, and that class will be the only one produced there.

Thus are our vintners, step by step, emerging from the chaos of inexperience, and acquiring additional knowledge.

Nearly every forward step was met by almost insurmountable difficulties, and most of the early vintners, having commenced without adequate means, and counting too certainly upon unreasonable and quick profits, became almost hopelessly discouraged by the long time that elapsed before their vineyards bore, then by the seemingly low prices their grapes realized, and, last, but not least, by the great outlay attendant upon wine-making.

Their troubles had only commenced when their vineyards began to give fruit. Those who had set out vineyards with the sole intention of selling their grapes for table use—and these were the majority—found the markets overcrowded, and the cost of transportation and commissions so high, that they were not left a fair profit for their industry, and were forced to make wine to save themselves.

Cellars had to be dug, houses erected, presses built, and casks procured: every thing had to be created, and almost without material. Coopers could not be had for love or money, neither could oak staves. Every available cask, pipe, and barrel was made use of, and extravagant prices paid for them. There were not enough, even at twelve and fourteen cents per gallon for second-hand casks, and from eighteen to twenty cents for new. The vintners became alarmed, meetings were held, and resolutions offered with a view to induce the importation of coopers and material. The first shift was to make vats of large size from redwood staves, and it was a timely thought, which saved many gallons of wine to the vintner. Gradually, through the persistent efforts of these pioneer vintners, material became plenty, and good coopers numerous; new casks declined in price to eight and nine cents per gallon, became abundant, and, at these prices, within the reach of every one.

The wine began slowly to find sale, though the quantity sold was in small lots, and at very low prices; still there was consolation in the fact that *some* wine could be sold—a fact that, a short time previous, but few, in their despondent mood, were willing to believe. Soon, whole crops found sale at fixed rates, which left a very fair profit to the producer; nor has this change stopped here, for the increase in production has become so rapid, that it is at this moment almost impossible to find any quantity of one-year-old wine in the hands of the producers, unless they make a point of keeping it for aging.

PART TWO

California has one advantage over any wine-producing country on the globe, and that is the certainty, constancy, and duration of her dry season. The grape is a fruit that needs, above all others, a warm sunshine, without interruption, from the time that the blossoms set forth their tender flowers, until they gradually develop into its rich, luscious fruit in October. This advantage has always existed here, as far back as our record extends, and no rain or hail ever destroyed the tender fruit. The sure and uninterrupted duration of this dry weather secures a crop without a chance of failure, and ripens the grape to perfection. One of the most serious drawbacks in all other parts of the world is the uncertainty of the seasons and entire variance from preceding ones, thus creating a great difference in the quality of the wine produced in successive vintages. This difference in quality is so great that it is quite common to find the prices vary from one to two hundred per cent. in the same district. The products of the renowned vineyards are known to have fluctuated even to a greater extent.

In Europe, they only reckon to secure in ten years one good crop and fine quality, and two more crops of fine quality, but small quantity; while seven vintages are reckoned as being of poor quality, small quantity, and total failures. In our State, the variation in quality seldom amounts to five per cent., while the most disastrous years have not lessened the crop below the ordinary yield more than twenty-five per cent. in quantity. This very variation in quantity can be fully known three months previous to the vintage, thus allowing the producer ample time to secure his casks, and furnishing him positive knowledge as to the number required. In other countries, even fourteen days before the vintage, there is no certainty of a crop; a wind, a rain, or a hail-storm is apt to occur at any moment and devastate the entire vintage. All is uncertainty there; nor has the vintner any possible means of positively ascertaining how many casks he must provide. In abundant years in the old countries the exchange has often been made of so many gallons of wine for an equal number of gallons' capacity of casks. The disadvantages of being forced to secure such immense quantities of casks in so limited a period are too easily perceived, and we certainly can not appreciate our own adavntage too much in being very differently situated.

Another great benefit derived from the long continuance of the dry weather, is the exemption from weeds in our vineyards after the final plowing. Thus all the nourishment and strength of the soil go wholly to their destination, the vine, and hence the vigorous appearance that even the most delicate imported varieties acquire even in our poorest soils. They necessarily bear much more. This circumstance will also explain, in a measure, why our cultivation does not cost as much per acre as that in European countries, though our labor is so much higher.

The advantage of our dry weather does not end here: it precludes the possibility of continued mildew, and allows the vintner to leave his vines unstaked, the bunches of grapes actually lying, and securely ripening, upon the very ground, without fear of frost or rotting. In this condition, the grapes mature sooner, are sweeter, and, it is believed, possess more flavor.

In Europe, of late years, there has grown into favor, and almost general use, the custom of gallizing the wines. This consists of adding certain amounts of sugar and water to a definite proportion of grapes, and is intended to increase the quantity of wine. This process was first conceived by

Count [J. A. C.] Chaptal, about the year 1801, and many years later was reduced to a practical form, by [M.] Petiot, in France, and Dr. [H. L. L.] Gall, in Germany. Two circumstances tended to bring this into practical use: the first was excusable enough, but not so the second. Count Chaptal, seeing the inequality of the seasons, the total or partial failures of the quality of the vintages, owing to a want of proper maturity in the grape when picked, and a lack of sugar in its natural juice, proposed to make an addition of cane or potato-sugar to this juice, and thus bring it up to a standard. He contended that the quality of the juice depended on the amount of sugar it contained, and claimed that, by making this addition, a good wine could be invariably produced. This process he called, "The manner of making good wines, both in good and poor years." The theory certainly presented itself in a very attractive and harmless manner to the wine-producers of Europe, and would have had no serious objections in its use, in such countries as could not sufficiently ripen their grapes to produce the required amount of sugar, to make the wine palatable, and sustain it in aging.

Had this process stopped there, it might have been excusable, but such was not the case; and, as one evil step leads to another, so did this process lead to another, which had no excuse whatever to offer, other than that it was harmless, and that in defrauding those who purchased it for pure grape wine, the harm was only the deception. Messrs. Petiot and Gall, both men of eminently practical minds, suggested, that, owing to the greater demand for wine than the supply could meet, why not make an addition of water to the juice, and bring the quality to the proper standard again by adding to the whole the necessary amount of sugar to guarantee its keeping quality.

THREE TRADE CARDS

ARPAD HARASZTHY & CO'S CHAMPAGNES.

o

We take great pride in recommending our pure and really superior Champagnes to the public generally. They are produced exactly as are all the high grade French Champagnes, by fermentation in the bottle, but, differently from their foreign competitors, are neither strengthened with spirits, nor flavored up in any manner, but are absolutely pure, and therefore, even when indiscreetly used, will never produce a headache.

o

THE ECLIPSE EXTRA DRY is a dry, delicate flavored, vivacious Wine, eminently suited for Parties, Dinners, and Clubs.

o

THE SPARKLING MUSCATEL is a luscious, rich, high flavored Wine, of the Moselle order, only much richer, and a great favorite with the ladies.

o

THE GRAND PRIZE, often called the PRIVATE CUVEE, is a medium dry, full flavored fine bodied Wine, and highly prized by all for these elegant qualities.

o

No true connoisseur can try these superior Champagnes without admiring them.

How splendidly I feel after
that bottle of
ECLIPSE Extra Dry.

FINE TABLE WINES.
Arpad Haraszthy & Co.
530 Washington Street, S. F., Cal.

"Anna, sweet Anna, I sing to
thee,"

In ECLIPSE Champagne.
In ECLIPSE Champagne !!

FINE TABLE WINES.
Arpad Haraszthy & Co.
530 Washington Street, S. F., Cal.

At first, they only doubled the quantity, but finally they brought their theory to such a practical point, that the amount of grapes which previously gave one gallon of pure juice was now made to yield five, and even six gallons of this so-called wine. The only requirement in this process was to press from the grapes all the juice that would flow, then pour upon the remaining skins sugar and water in defined proportions, and allow it to ferment; the resulting liquid was then run into barrels, and the addition of sugared water was again made successively from four to six times, according to the judgment of the manufacturer. This liquid was sold for wine, and has been exported by the million gallons to all countries of the world ever since the process was put into practical operation, many years ago. The United States is one of the heaviest consumers of this class of wine, which arrives in every one of its ports by the thousand casks, under the name of "Cargo Claret."

California is entirely free from the use of such expedients, nor is it likely that she will have to resort to them until her millions of vineland will have been planted. Our grape-juice requires no addition of sugar, either to make it palatable or give it the keeping qualities. Our grapes ripen and over-ripen securely every year, without the chance of a failure, and they can be brought to produce any fermentable amount of pure grape-sugar by simply leaving them to hang on the vine a longer time, without shelter and without danger, for the rains seldom set in until the vintage has been closed from one month to six weeks.

As to adding both water and sugar to produce more, our vineyards bear too abundantly to warrant such a proceeding, even if the cost of such additions were not greater than that of the pure grape-juice. But this cost is greater, no matter what quality of sugar is used, or how cheap it could at present be purchased. Twelve pounds of grapes can be procured for twelve cents, and contain, or will give by expressing, at the lowest average, two and one-half pounds of sugar, costing four and eight-tenths cents per pound; while sugar, even without duty, would cost from thirty to fifty per cent. more, counting upon the use of the commonest quality. There being no gain, at present, nor possibly for the future, in the adulteration with sugared water, it is not likely the practice will be made use of in California until sugar costs much less or grapes much more, neither of which is likely to occur soon; so the grape-juice will still remain the cheapest article with which to adulterate our wines.

The above is probably the most innocent adulteration used in the European wines. There is one practice, allowed by custom and carried on almost universally, which is postively injurious, and that is the addition of alcohol, which is made, in the most unscrupulous proportions, to nearly all wines destined for export and shipped in casks. This is particularly the case with the cheap French clarets that are used in such enormous quantities in every part of the globe. By a recent regulation, made between the years 1864 and 1866, French shippers are allowed to add to all wines that they export, five per cent. of absolute alcohol. That they make use of this privilege, is amply proved by the high percentage of alcohol found in all their wines that reach us. This fact will explain why French clarets are usually drank with water, and are better tasting when used in that way. The French Government does not, however, allow this addition of alcohol to wines that are to be consumed at home, except in the wines produced in seven departments, which it is known will spoil without this addition. It evidently has more regard for the health of its own subjects than that of foreign people who pay it tribute.

The wines of our State, owing to the great abundance of sugar produced from the grape, naturally contain a large proportion of alcohol, and require no such additions; in fact, of late years, it has been one of the principal studies of the wine-makers to devise some natural way of diminishing the proportion of alcohol, in order to produce lighter wines. Two very easy methods of attaining this end have been found. The first method was proposed by the writer of this sketch, in 1862, and consisted in picking the grapes at an earlier period than was usually done — at a period when they had attained a sufficient quantity of sugar to produce a wine containing from ten to eleven per cent. of alcohol after fermentation. As the amount of alcohol depended entirely upon the amount of sugar, this method could very easily be put into practice, and during later years it has been extensively done in those parts of the State best suited for producing light wines. The wines so made at first lacked character and, seemingly, body; but as they began to mature by age, they were found to contain both, and acquire a fresh, agreeable flavor, far superior to the wines made in the old manner from over-ripe grapes. Besides, they were found to conduct themselves better as to clarification, and were generally less apt to acquire those diseases that the heavier wines are liable to.

The second method consists in planting those varieties of grapes which are known to produce light wines; in other words, such grapes as do not produce a large quantity of sugar. The result in both methods is the same, though the latter is unquestionably the better, for those varieties of grapes which lack in sugar generally abound in flavor, and the wine made from them almost always acquires a fine, delicate bouquet. These wines, while new, are harsh and exceedingly tart, but age does away with both objections, and they then become spicy, agreeable, inviting, and do not cloy, as is the case with heavier wines. It has been ascertained, by repeated trials, that the wines produced by either method, only require skill in their management, and need no doctoring, to make them keep; age alone improves their qualities, and when shipped they are found to improve most by the longest voyages. They have been known to keep well, even under the most neglectful management and entire absence of skill.

Above and beyond the ability and advantage we have of producing all kinds of grapes to perfection, of making from them wines that are pleasant, inviting to the taste, and which will keep, with but little skill and care, for years, whose limit has not yet been found, we still have a greater advantage over European vintners in the cheapness of our cultivation. Labor, material, and interest are all very high with us; but, nevertheless, the setting out and cultivation of an acre of vineyard costs less in California than it does in France. For this we are as much indebted to our improved means of cultivation as to the nature of our climate.

All labor, in the majority of the wine districts of Europe, is done by hand. We use the horse and plow, while they use the prong-hoe and spade, and they actually dig and hoe up their entire vineyards, with few exceptions. After our spring cultivation is over, we need not go into our vineyards, and, having no summer rains, weeding is not necessary, and still their freeness from weeds and clean appearance strike the stranger with surprise. Owing, on the contrary, to the wet season of Europe, the vine-dressers are constantly kept among the vines, trying to give them a clean appearance; but, in spite of all their efforts, they but imperfectly succeed, and their vineyards never possess that appearance of high and perfect cultivation that is so apparent in our own.

But we have stated that the plantation of a vineyard and its keeping cost more in France than in California; and, to prove this, we will make extracts from a well-known and reliable authority upon the subject, M. [Jules] Guyot:

Cost in France of an Hectare (2½ Acres) of Vineyards after the Seventh Year:

Purchase of one hectare of land	$200
Expense of first year	200
" second year	100
" third year	171
" fourth year	229
" fifth year	120
(besides $40, being product of vintage of fourth year.)	
Expense of sixth year	100
(besides $80, being product of vintage of fifth year.)	
Expense of seventh year	30
(besides $160, being product of vintage of sixth year.)	
Total expense	$1,150

This does not include interest, which will amount to about $240 more, making the total cost of one hectare of vineyard, in the seventh year, $1,390, or $556 per acre. These different items include all the material, manure, and the extraordinary preparation of the soil, so essential in Europe to produce good crops. In the estimate made for the usual cultivation, the cost per acre amounts to $35 after the seventh year. And by this same ordinary and usual mode of cultivation, the yield is reckoned at about four hundred gallons per acre — a very large estimate, in our opinion.

Cost in California of an Acre of Vineyard after the Seventh Year:

Purchase of one acre land	$50		
Planting and cultivating, first year	30		
Cultivating, second year	10		
" third year	10		
" fourth year	12	Value of crop	$35
" fifth year	15	Value of crop	42
" sixth year	15	Value of crop	49
" seventh year	15	Value of crop	66
Direct outlay	$157	Direct income	$192
Interest at 12 per cent. per annum on outlay	99	Int. at 12 per ct. on income	52
Total outlay	$256	Total income	$244

Leaving the actual cost of the vineyard in California, after the seventh year, at $12 per acre, against $556 in France, in spite of expensive labor and high rates of interest. The cultivation of a full-bearing vineyard is less than $15 per acre with us, against $35 in France, and our crops throughout the State, on an average, will be considerably over rather than under four hundred gallons per acre.

These figures, for California, leave such a margin, that no difficulty would be met with in securing any number of persons who would be willing to undertake the contract, at these rates, for setting and cultivating up to the seventh year. The cost of the land alone is overestimated about $20. The comparison of these figures leads us to the strange result, that at the eighth year the Californian starts his acre of vineyard with an investment of $12, his interest on that sum being $1.44 yearly; while the French vintner starts his acre of vineyard with an investment, from the same year, of $556, and his yearly interest, at five per cent., will amount to $27.80.

There is one very great cost in the cultivation of the vine

in Europe which is dispensed with entirely in our State, and that is the *staking* of the vines. It is true that some of our vine-growers stake their vines, in imitation of the European mode; but even these only continue this practice till the vine is six or seven years old, when the stakes are discarded. In Europe, the vines are staked each spring, and in the autumn, when the vintage is over, the stakes are pulled up and piled away for protection from winter—a very onerous task, and a costly one. To this is joined another work, which we never have to do, that of tying up the vines, to keep the grapes from rotting, as they would by lying on the ground. Many more details could be cited, showing our advantages; but these are sufficient to give a general appreciation of the greater economy of our mode of cultivation over that practiced in European vineyards.

The Fathers planted their vines all the way from eight to sixteen feet apart in the square, and there has been much controversy among viniculturists as to the proper distance for planting. In this, as in many other things, one general rule can not be laid down: the person planting should not be governed by a hobby of distances, but should be guided by the nature of the soil, and by the character of the species of vine planted. As a general rule, vines planted in rich soil run to wood, and should be planted far apart; in lighter soils, they should be planted closer together. The old method was to plant in squares; but the more recent plantations have most all been made in rows, which manner is the more rational, and presents, among many other advantages, that of allowing the plantation of a greater number of vines to the acre, without discarding the use of the plow. The usual distance between the vines, in vineyards thus set out, is four feet one way and six feet the other. It has been found that a greater number of vines to the acre, within reasonable limits, produce more than a less number. The old plantations contained generally 680 vines per acre, while the new ones contain 1,000 and 1,800 vines to the same space. The following are the average yields, for the whole State, in these different modes of planting, when the vines are seven years old:

680 vines per acre	10 lbs per vine, 6,800 lbs grapes.
1,000 vines per acre	8 lbs per vine, 8,000 lbs grapes.
1,800 vines per acre	5 lbs per vine, 9,000 lbs grapes.

It is now conceded, in those localities where the experiments were made with these different modes of growing the vines, that the ten pounds of grapes produced by two vines are superior in every respect to the ten pounds produced by a single vine on the same amount of space. The pruning of the vines costs about $4 per thousand; the hoeing and suckering, when properly done, about as much more: so that the expense, on a greater number of vines, per acre, would increase somewhat the cost of cultivation; but this would be more than made good by the increased quantity of grapes. The cost of picking is nearly $1.25 per ton, and that of hauling, within a distance of five miles, about $1 more, making, in all, $2.25 per ton.

The average price of grapes is $1 per hundred pounds, delivered, and the gross income of a vineyard containing 680 vines would be $68. Deducting picking and hauling, $8, and cultivation, $15, would leave a yearly net income of $45 per acre on an investment of $112 and interest up to the fourth year. This reckoning is based upon the blue Mission grape; and where the vineyard is planted with choicer varieties, the income is from two to four times greater, according to the variety. When wine is made, instead of selling the grapes, the net income can be reckoned upon as amounting to at least fifty per cent. more. This increase holds good with wines made from the choicer kinds of grapes.

In California, mildew has only made its appearance in low, wet places, where vineyards never should have been planted, or in exceedingly wet years; but has never spread, even when sulphur was not used — it being a very rare occurrence to have it in two successive seasons on the same vineyard, no matter how unfavorably that vineyard may be located. It was also thought by many that the importation of foreign vines would be attended by the introduction of their diseases; but this fear has so far proved groundless, though ample time has elapsed for such diseases to show themselves. It seems that our climate and soil have not only an invigorating power, but also a purifying one over all imported vines: the trunks become robust, the vines larger, and the leaves greener than in their native countries.

We have already alluded to the necessity of ascertaining the adaptability of certain varieties to the various soils and numerous climates of our State. This discovery for each locality is of the most vital importance, and only through such a result can the highest possible excellence be attained in the quality of the wine produced. Many varieties do well in meagre, gravelly soils, which will bear but indifferently in cold, moist, or rich soils, and *vice versa*. There are but few vineyards in the State, that were planted within the last twelve years, which do not contain from ten to fifteen varieties of vines, and we can therefore hope, that, at no very distant period, the best varieties will be discovered for each district.

In fact, we are now upon the very verge of acquiring this important knowledge, for everywhere throughout the different districts, *grafting*—that great revolutionizing agent— is actively employed; every year, the number of varieties descreases in each vineyard—the few are chosen from the many—and in a few seasons the entire character of the wines will be changed and the proper type found. As interest and labor are so high with us, we have to look further, in making our plantations, than the sole production of quality. To it we must join quantity, else the profits will not be compensating, in competition with European wine countries. Our ambition must be to produce as fine a quality as they do, and a much greater quantity; and, by a judicious and rational use of the graft, it is in our power to attain this.

When two varieties of grapes in the same vineyard, one producing a superior quality of wine, but is a poor bearer, while the other bears abundantly, but produces a poor quality, the former should be grafted upon the latter, and by this method secure the advantages of both kinds. This is the judicious use of the art of grafting, while the rational use consists in setting out the prolific-bearing vines, with the preconceived intent to graft upon them the finer variety, when the proper moment arrives. It is true, that grafting is tedious and expensive; but the result will give ample reward for all the cost, labor, and expense.

After years of patient waiting and experiment, we have, at last, secured that perfection of fruit which excites the wonder and admiration of all strangers who visit our State. Though our greatest triumphs have been with the fruit of the vine itself, still, we have not been backward in manufacturing that fruit into wine. And this was the most difficult task of all. Our wine-makers undertook it without knowledge, and almost without capital. Our climate being different from that of any other part of the world, even those who had previous experience in wine-producing countries were, at first, baffled and doomed to disappointment. Much had to be forgotten, that was held valuable in other countries, and more had to be learned. The old, slow, and burdensome methods of Europe were improved upon, and what was objectionable gradually became obsolete. Every thing was, generally, done on a grander scale: machinery was introduced, in the crushing of grapes — presses were improved — greater quantities of wine were made, and finer and larger casks were constructed. The same improvements were made in our wine-vaults and press-houses, to whose solid and cleanly appearance we point with pride. Such, in fact, have been our advances, that the casks used in Europe to manufacture wine in, we consider even too small to make our sales in.

These rapid improvements are, in a measure, owing to our isolated position, where necessity truly becomes the mother of invention; and, in a greater measure, to the un-selfish manner in which our wine-makers meet each other, neighbor striving to help neighbor, and imparting freely all personal experiences. This open and generous inter-change of acquired knowledge is a feature, not only with our wine-makers, but is perceived in every industrial enter-prise of our State.

The early varieties of grapes begin to make their appear-ances in the San Francisco market about the first week in July. These, of course, are not made into wine, but are consumed at table. The vintage begins at different periods in the various districts, and, even in these districts, the vintage begins in one vineyard sooner or later than in the adjoining one, according to the variety of grapes with which it is planted. The earliest vintages, however, generally be-gin about the first of September, and the latest about the end of October. Our average first heavy rain, for the last twelve years, has not fallen before the first of December; and, during the same period, only in six years have we had slight showers during the month of October, their average being the 17th of that month, and rather helped the ungathered grapes than harmed them. This will show, that even the most dilatory wine-makers have ample time to secure their vintages, without fear of loss from such sources.

The grapes in the northern portion of the State are picked by Chinamen, who will each pick an average of fifteen hundred pounds per day. They always board themselves, and are paid, generally, $1 per day. The grapes are gathered into light wooden boxes, which will hold about fifty pounds each. When full, these boxes are hauled to the press-house, where they are emptied into a screen, and the grapes, becoming detached from their stems, fall through the screen, and are crushed between two revolving rollers. The bruised grapes fall on an inclined platform underneath, and part of the juice runs off without further pressing, and is conducted into casks.

There remains, however, a considerable quantity of juice in the crushed and dripping grapes. To extract this, they are removed to the press, and the juice running from it is added to that which previously came from the crusher. The skins of the grapes, after being thoroughly pressed, still contain a considerable amount of saccharine matter, and are thrown into a vat, where, after being covered with water, they are allowed to ferment, and, in due time, the liquid resulting from this fermentation is distilled into brandy. The juices coming from the crusher and press begin to ferment violently about ten or twelve hours after the pressing; and, if the fermenting vaults are at the proper temperature — between seventy and seventy-five degrees Fahrenheit — it ceases in fifteen days. The muddy appearance lessens, disappears entirely, and the wine is made. This is the process followed in the making of white wines from the blue or black grapes.

When red wines are made, the juice is not separated from the crushed grapes, but the whole is thrown into a vat, where the juice ferments upon the skins. As the coloring matter is contained on the inside of the skins, this contact during fermentation, which lasts from four to ten days, necessarily communicates that color to the juice. When the fermentation ceases, the red juice has become wine, and is then drawn into casks. This, combined with cleanliness and attention, is, really, all there is in wine-making in our State. The care to be bestowed upon the wine, after fermentation, is another matter, and is, of itself, a great and complicated art, very difficult to be communicated.

The wines are drawn from their settlings, into clean casks, about the beginning of January, and again in the month of March. After this last racking, they are generally sold to the various San Francisco wine-houses, the wine-merchants all preferring, if they have room, to remove the new wine to their own vaults as soon as possible, to give it the necessary care while ripening. The average annual cost of keeping red and white wines in San Francisco is about ten cents per gallon, including storage, care, evaporation, and interest upon cost of wine and cask.

The bulk of California wines is sold to the consumer after they are one, and before they are two, years old. This is a bad practice, which necessity alone forced upon the wine-merchants, and which, we are glad to state, is fast passing away. To attain their full excellence, the lighter California wines should be bottled when two years old, and left to mature in bottle for a period of two years more. Thus managed, they become excellent, even from the blue Mission grape, and are far superior to the good class of French wines. The aging in bottle developes a bouquet and flavor that are never acquired in the cask alone.

Not accountable for Leakage Damage or Loss by Transportation. All claims for disagreement with Invoice must be made within Five days after receipt of Goods.

SAN FRANCISCO, *July 6* 1887.

Mesrs *E. A. Nicholson and Co.*

DR.

ARPAD HARASZTHY & CO.

ESTABLISHED 1863

ARPAD HARASZTHY   HENRY EPSTEIN

Producers of Champagne by the only Natural Process; that of Fermentation in the Bottle.

DEALERS IN ALL KINDS OF

CALIFORNIA WINES, BRANDIES AND CHAMPAGNE.

PROPRIETORS OF THE I X L BITTERS.

530 WASHINGTON ST.

P.O. BOX 1685

TERMS:

10   Gal. Zinfandel   Cos⁵   10.50

PART THREE

That the making of wine may be done in a proper, as well as profitable manner, every available portion of the grape should be made use of. All the juice that can be easily pressed out should be made into wine, and the remnants of the grapes after the pressing should be used to produce brandy. Unfortunately for the wine-makers of the State, the laws and regulations made by Congress for governing distillers generally, are entirely impracticable as applied to the distillation of the product of grapes. These regulations have proved in practice to be so onerous and burdensome to this class of distillers, that not one-quarter of the brandy is manufactured even from the refuse of the press that should be made. Wastefulness is never considered profitable, but if these Federal regulations are carried out (as they are), it is almost an advantage to the wine-maker to throw away the leavings of the press. And this is just what has been done ever since the unwise legislation of Congress has been enforced. The wine-makers everywhere, with hardly any exceptions, simply press out the juice as much as is practicable, and then throw away the balance, thereby losing, for themselves and the community, the value of ten proof gallons of brandy to every original ton of grapes. Instead of there being, as there should be, a small still attached to every vineyard, no matter what its size, there can hardly be found one to every hundred vineyards, under the present regulations. This is all wrong; and a strenuous, as well as united effort, should be made to bring Congress to a just understanding of the damage that its inapplicable rules are causing.

As a single illustration of the absurdity of the law, we will mention the capacity regulation. This consists in making a survey of the still, and fixing thereby its capacity for

49

distilling per diem. Now, some of our wines will yield six-teen per cent. absolute alcohol, while the remnants from the pressings, in many instances, do not yield five per cent. The difference is eleven per cent. when half and half are distilled, and much greater when more of the weaker wine is distilled; in fact, it is impossible to reach the Govern-ment survey with any thing but a right strong wine, and hence but little other is distilled with profit.

There is another part of these regulations, which is a very heavy burden to wine-makers: it is that which compels them to pay the Internal Revenue tax upon their brandy so soon after distillation. This tax amounts to two-fifths of the salable value of the brandy, and its tendency is to make the producer dispose of it at the earliest possible opportun-ity. He can not keep it to acquire the proper quality by age, when, besides its original cost to him, he has to add one hundred per cent. more in the shape of a cash outlay; so, instead, it is hurried upon the market long before it has attained any of the necessary qualities. The Govern-ment should build, or cause to be built, bonded ware-houses, at convenient distances, in the wine districts, where these brandies might be bonded and be left to attain age, and only exact the taxes thereon when removed, or after a reasonable number of years, say from two to four. The distillers of grapes throughout the State would immediately avail themselves of this privilege, and in a few years we would seldom meet any raw California brandy. It is even more important that brandy should have age than wine, for when new it is uninviting, and even unpalatable.

There is still one thing more which should be allowed to grape distillers: that of exemption of taxes upon all brandies exported without the limits of the United States. If this were done, there would hardly be a limit to the trade that would be carried on when the business of exportation had once properly begun. Our brandies would then be within the reach of the whole world—France not excepted. Pure and entire grape brandy could be sold, if exempt from taxation, at eighty cents per gallon—less, even, than it is sold for in France. It would, from its very cheapness, immediately become an article of export to all the countries bordering upon the Pacific Ocean. All our pure wines and grapes would be distilled into brandy; the refuse would no longer be thrown away; hundreds of thousands of dollars would be saved to the community, and as many more returned as a result of our export. Wines themselves would bring fairer prices, not being in competition with those only fit for the still, and a new era of prosperity would begin. It is to be hoped that proper representations will be made to Congress with regard to this great interest of our State.

As to the progress we have made in the improvement of the qualities of our brandies, it has been equal to that made in our wines. We have no brandies of any considerable age; but still, limited quantities are procurable which are from three to four years old, and which, though not presenting the exact taste of any particular brand of Cognac, nevertheless are just as pleasant and drinkable as most of them of the same age, and of less than one-quarter the price. It is not essential that our brandies resemble exactly any one kind of French Cognac, for no two brands from France are counterparts. Each house dealing in Cognac has adopted a certain flavoring, and they all differ. Our distillers have not got so far yet as to make a general use of flavoring in their brandies; and we must say, that when these are properly distilled and refined, aided by resonable age, they require no artificial flavoring, and become rich, mellow, and inviting.

There have been various methods and processes suggested and tried, to give the qualities of age to brandies and wines. One process consists of heating the wines or brandies; and another, of freezing them. One consists of pumping air into the wine; while another pumps it out. Each and all claim perfection for their processes; but those who have tried them thoroughly have condemned all these expedients, as entirely inefficient in producing the benefits promised. The only change effected was a vapid softness, that in no manner resembled the qualities acquired by age.

Age develops the flavor, through a long, slow, and gradual change of the natural ingredients of the wine; and when this flavor has become fully and agreeably developed, it is called bouquet. There is no artificial process yet invented which can produce this result. It is much to be regretted that many of our wine-makers are so enterprising, because they have been, and still will be, victimized by every sanguine process-inventor who comes along. Thousands of gallons of good wine have thus been spoiled annually, by people who wish their wines to acquire all the qualities that age alone can communicate. But we learn as we grow older; and the good days of these would-be inventors have passed. We are fast coming to the conclusion, that Nature's laboratory, managed by Time, is the most perfect of all; and man can follow closely, but not excel, nor even equal, Nature's silent work.

During the first few years of grape culture in California, considerable quantities of wine were made, and put upon the market; and, as it did not find an immediate sale, the producers became almost disheartened. They had serious cause for fear, as the California wines had not yet been extensively introduced, and the consumption was still very limited. The wine merchants would gladly have purchased, but the limited means they possessed were already invested, the banks refused them credit, and capitalists were unwilling to invest their money in what they considered a hazardous business. Little did either the bankers or capitalists imagine to what an extent this enterprise would be carried in a few short years. Neither did they know that wine was one of the best and safest securities upon which money could be loaned; for, instead of decreasing in value, it improves, becoming more and more valuable as it grows older, and in greater proportion than the cost of care, storage, and interest. But bankers and capitalists begin to understand the real value of such security, and but little difficulty is now experienced by wine-merchants in obtaining all needed accommodation.

The dealers of San Francisco, after receiving and storing the wines until they attain the age they desire them to acquire, clarify them, and then offer them to the trade. This is done either in bottles, in demijohns, or in small barrels, according to the respective classes of trade they are engaged in. Very large quantities of wine are shipped to the Eastern States, *via* Cape Horn and the Isthmus of Panama. A great deal is also sent overland, by railroad, to the Territories, and the States in the Mississippi Valley. The business with these latter has increased in the most encouraging manner, ever since the railroad began to carry freight.

The reputation of California wines in the Eastern States is at this moment undergoing one of the severest trials that can be put upon the product of any country: that of palming off upon the confiding public spurious, inferior, and barefaced imitations of the same, which never saw the soil of our State, nor resemble our wines in any particular. This unscrupulous traffic is carried on openly throughout the Eastern States, and millions of gallons of these compounds over and above the actual product of this State are probably sold. It is of the greatest importance to our wine-makers to ascertain by what means this evil can be stopped, or at least mitigated, else it will soon become difficult to retain the fair reputation we have already gained. This imposition can only be practiced upon those who are not accustomed to our wines; and it is so unskillfully manufactured that it is a matter of surprise how any wine-drinker can be deceived by it. The basis is generally cider, while the other ingredients are alum, cream-tartar, sulphuric acid, catechu, sugar, water, alcohol, and logwood, and the resulting liquid is flavored and called wine. It is labeled German Hock, Château-Yquem, or California White Wine, according to that which is most in vogue at the time of manufacture.

Another circumstance, much to be regretted, is the universal custom of Eastern houses, who deal in California wines, to purchase the cheapest, not the best, of our wines; and these are, of course, offered to their customers as having been selected by themselves from the finest products of our State. It seems as if these houses aim more at the extent of their immediate sales than the foundation of a future reputation — striving to outdo each other in the decreased prices, and not in the superiority of the wines offered; every year sending out their agents, who purchase the lowest-priced wines that can be found. It will be necessary for some of our own houses of known reputation, in pure self-defense, to establish depots of their own in the principal cities of the East. This is constantly urged by Eastern men of influence, who are all loud in their praise of the wines they find here, but equally loud in their denunciations of those which are sold as California wines throughout the Atlantic States.

It was once thought that New York would be the future

central distributing point of all our wines, but the potent influence of the railroad has already made itself felt, and it now becomes more and more evident that San Francisco is destined to occupy that important position. The orders which formerly were filled in New York, are now being filled in San Francisco; and this extends not only to the States of the Mississippi Valley, but even to those bordering on the Atlantic. These direct orders would be more frequent and to a larger extent, if our rates of interest were lower and a more extended credit were given, as is customary with Eastern houses. The difference in currency also acts as a drawback. But even in the face of these inequities, the change is being rapidly effected.

The value of our wine from any particular district, or from the whole State, has not yet been definitely determined, and we are therefore without a positive wine market. The preferences of the consumers can alone establish true values; and these will be ascertained by time and experience. The vineyards which rank as the very best, one year, may have to recede from that position the next season, and give the palm to a new vineyard, which is bearing for the first time, or whose superiority remains unknown till the comparison has been made.

Our wines are generally considered cheap, but they are not as cheap as some of them should be, nor as high-priced as a few will surely become. It is of the greatest importance that we have wines that can be used instead of tea or coffee, and at a reduced price they can take the place of both these articles. That wine is healthier and contains more nourishment than either, is a fact upheld by the most reliable chemists and physicians. Growers should not receive less than their present profits: and hence we suggest the necessity of planting varieties, which, at the same cost in cultivation, will produce more to the acre; that they secure casks at a less cost, money at lower rates of interest, cheaper labor, and more perfect machinery.

The wine-merchant must also practice economy — secure low interest and increase the amount of his sales, so that his profits on each gallon shall be less, but in the aggregate more. It is by such united efforts that wine can be sold cheaper to the consumer; and when this has been accomplished, this industry will attain that firm and important position that it is destined to occupy in our commerce. The higher prices for certain wines will be established by known preferences, and limited by the ability to supply the demand.

Heretofore our wines have reached the consumer under the too general and too sweeping denomination of "California wine." This, however, is now fast being done away with, and each district is being recognized as producing certain characteristics of its own, and is receiving such reputation as its merit entitles it to. Thus, we have Sonoma, Anaheim, Los Angeles, Napa, and El Dorado wines, each bearing its peculiar characteristics, and purchased on that account. Gradually the classification will advance, and the distinction made be greater among the vineyards in each district. Even now this distinction is made by several of the prominent wine-houses in San Francisco, who are willing to pay an increased percentage for wines from certain vineyards in the same district.

We are now enabled to point out with great precision the character of wine which our best-known districts are capable of producing, and there are probably but few wines made in any part of the globe whose general characteristics can not be reproduced very closely, in some portion of our State. For instance, Sonoma is best adapted to produce white wines, resembling those of Germany; the upper part of Napa Valley and certain portions of Santa Clara County will make excellent clarets; the Sacramento Valley, near the foot of the inclosing hills, is destined to produce our future sweet muscats; El Dorado County is best adapted to the production of a wine resembling the far-famed Burgundy; Solano County produces a wine which is a natural port; San Joaquin and Stanislaus counties give wines which closely resemble, both in flavor and taste, the best Madeira, but they have to attain an age of from five to six years before this taste is sufficiently developed; Anaheim and certain portions of Los Angeles County produce light white wines, which very closely resemble those of Chablis, in France, and they, too, must be some four years old before this peculiarity shows itself distinctly, and the last two years should be in bottle. Many other districts will, in time, manifest their characteristics, and be classified.

PART FOUR

There always has been, and is at present, a lack of reliable statistics concerning our entire vinicultural interest. The most authentic information that can be obtained comes from a few public-spirited men, engaged in the business, in different parts of the State. The official statistics are wholly incorrect, and often absurd; and this has been proved by comparing the official returns with the facts collected by reliable men, in single districts. Thus the *State Register* for 1857 gives Sonoma and Mendocino counties 170,000 vines, and in the following year only 87,000; whereas, instead of a decrease in the amount, there was an increase of 400,000 in Sonoma County alone. In the same manner, Sutter County is made to show 85,000 less in 1858 than in 1857, which is known to be incorrect. Even taking these very inaccurate figures, the *State Register* shows an increase for the entire State of 2,000,000 vines from 1857 to 1858, and gives the total amount at 4,000,000 vines in the latter year. Taking for granted that our increase has continued since then in the same ratio — and we know it to have been greater in almost every county but Los Angeles — we would now possess about 30,000,000 vines, and the number certainly is not less. The last official report places the number at 23,000,000 vines, but gross inaccuracies are found in several well-known counties, which give us just cause to consider the total amount under-estimated.

The inaccuracy of the reports concerning the amount of wine produced is still greater than that of the number of vines. Sonoma County was reported to have made 209,000 gallons in the vintage of 1870, while a detailed statement of the different vineyards showed an actual production of over 650,000 gallons. The error for Napa County was even greater than the above. The blame for these inaccuracies can not justly be laid entirely to the Assessors: they are given a certain rule by which to gather statistics, are not paid for extra work, and so if they carry out the general tenor of their instructions, they consider their duty accomplished. The burdens upon our country people have become so onerous that they are exceedingly shy of all Government officials, be they State or Federal, and it is wonderful how poor they become as soon as such officials put in an appearance. The number of the vines becomes insignificant, they being taxed as improvements, while the number of gallons of wine that are made is hardly worth while taking down, since each gallon is taxed as personal property.

The vintner feels these taxes more than would the farmer, because he has had to struggle so hard and wait so long before reaping any benefit at all from his vineyard. And the severe taxation upon our viniculturists is decidedly wrong: they should be taxed far less than the mere cultivators of grain, as they are, at this present time, far more valuable in forming a permanent population. The farmer, as is very often the case, can gather two, three, or four harvests, and then depart to another portion of the State, where the land is said to be richer. The vintner, as soon as he plants his vines, has chosen his future home, and his interests immediately extend over the welfare of the entire neighborhood.

Vineyards have been sold within the last twelve months at the rate of $250 to $400 per acre, according as they were wholly planted with Mission, or in part with the choicer imported varieties of vines. The prices are also somewhat governed by the district, and the distance from, as well as the convenience of reaching, the principal market. These prices do not include any improvements other than the vines and fences; dwellings, wine-vaults, press-houses, etc., having an additional value. The following estimate will give an average showing of the value of thirty acres of vineyard, together with improvements, and all apparatus necessary for wine-making:

Dwelling-house and furniture	$2,000
Press-house and wine-vaults	1,500
Barn and outhouses	500
Horses, wagon, plows, etc.	1,000
Casks, vats, presses, etc.	2,000
Thirty acres vineyard, at $300	9,000
Total, complete	$16,000

This statement shows that the cost of improvements and material necessary in wine-making and cultivation is equal to seven-ninths of the value of the vines, and will enable us to make a close estimate of the sum invested in California in this pursuit. Before proceeding, it must be remembered that at least one-half of the vines planted are of the finer varieties, and consequently much more valuable than the Mission grape. The quantity produced being equal, and the wine made bringing fifty per cent. more, the vines should be estimated fifty per cent. higher:

15,000,000 Mission vines, at 40 cents	$6,000,000
15,000,000 imported vines, at 60 cents	9,000,000
Improvements, seven-ninths additional	11,666,666
Last vintage, 6,000,000 gallons wine, at 35 cents per gallon	2,100,000
200,000 gallons grape brandy, at $1.50 per gallon	300,000
One-third of previous vintage, 1,600,000 gallons, still on hand, at 50 cents per gallon	800,000
Total amount invested	$29,866,666

If to this we add the amount employed by the different wine-merchants of the State, in casks, stock on hand, etc., the sum would be increased over $1,000,000, making the total valuation about $31,000,000. And the future annual increase of the investment will probably not fall short of $2,000,000, rather more than less.

The State derives the greatest benefits from the plantation of vineyards, as they have been planted during the last ten years — that is, on the hill-sides and on those lands too steep to cultivate with any thing else, or so poor that nothing else will grow. Thus the vineyards of the future will all be planted upon the mountain-sides, and interfere in no manner with the grain-lands. Millions of acres that are now covered with *chapurral* and *manzanita*-bushes will become utilized; for just those spots where these bushes grow, if there is any soil at all, are the very finest for vineyards. Nothing else will generally grow in such places, except these bushes and a short, tufted grass, that here and there seems to cling to the ground for dear existence. The vine, however, not only thrives, but actually luxuriates upon it. If the roots are only nourished with enough moisture during the first twelve months, all is right and sure; thereafter they push forward and downward where the moisture never fails, even through the most minute crevices of rocks or cement, in a manner most wonderful to behold.

In gravelly soils the roots of vines seven years old have been found thirty feet below the surface, and they have been found half that distance in crevices of the most compact cement. They extend everywhere, and where they find resistance they creep around, and attain their end at the last. It is by this culture that our thousands of now idle steep and rugged hills and mountains will become transformed into producers of value, and the laborious and patient owner will reap from them harvests of gold. From bleak and barren wastes they will become clothed in the fresh green of the vine, and their sides be dotted with prosperous and happy homes.

The cultivation of the vine in our State is, or rather will become, a greater benefit when population shall be more dense, when land is not so easily obtained, and will be more needed than at present. Then such pursuits will be followed as will best give a living on the smallest parcels of land; and the culture of the vine, in this respect, has but few equals. To make a comparison with grain, it will be found that twenty acres of vineyard will give a better income than one hundred acres planted in grain. One man can do all the cultivation of twenty acres of vineyard without help, while the fact is very different with grain; and to continue the comparison, in many parts of the State—especially in those places situated near the chief outlets of trade—good grain-land is worth, per acre, nearly two-thirds that of an old, full-bearing vineyard.

To these advantages in favor of the vine-culture, add that of the certainty of a crop, in wet or dry seasons, cold or hot. See, for instance, the result of the last vintage: after two successive dry seasons, we had one of the largest crops that was ever gathered in the State. The grain, in most parts of the State, did not even give a return of the seed planted; while the vines actually doubled the yield of the previous year, in most of the wine districts; nor was this increase effected by a loss in quality, for that, too, was better than ever before. Nor is it hard to explain either circumstance. The older vines were, of course, noticed as having borne the most: it was because their roots had gone down so far that they remained unaffected by the drought on the surface—they had found their moisture below. That they are better is owing to that same dryness, which did not allow so considerable an amount of glutinous matter to be absorbed by the roots; hence the rapid and easy clarification of the wines of the last vintage. They are more delicate, and freer to the palate, than they have ever been known to be. The wines of 1871 will long be remembered by connoisseurs as the finest we have yet produced.

This fact — that the wine-producers have secured a large crop, as well as one of superior quality, after two dry seasons — has, within the last few months, caused new inquiry as to the vine-culture of the State, and given an unexpected stimulus to proposed plantations. Our population is undergoing a radical change — is losing that restless shiftlessness, that willingness to take great risks for the chance of a great profit. The desire is gaining upon us to have less profits, but to have them sure. We are losing, as a community, that inordinate desire for riches, and acquiring that for comfort, ease, quiet — in short, all that the word Home can convey. And here is a pursuit that can, and does, satisfy these longings. That it be profitably and properly carried on, it must not be conducted in the manner of a mere speculation, though it is an excellent one; but it must be conducted with the sole view of making it the seat of a future home. It wants personal care and attention; and, when this is accorded, the management of a vineyard and its products is no longer a task, but becomes a pleasure, whose growth almost reaches to infatuation.

People must not go into the business of grape-raising, as many have done, with the view of making immense fortunes. This is not a gambling, but a legitimate pursuit, and only gives a percentage in the shape of income upon the investment. Nor must those about to engage in it demand or expect too much income from their vines. Many people have engaged, and are still engaging, in the business, who, with the possession of fifteen or twenty acres, expect to live in the style of bankers; and, if the income from their small vineyards does not suffice, they become disgusted, and condemn the pursuit. This class should not own vineyards, but engage, with the same capital, in the banking business, and learn from that what a legitimate income is.

The cultivation of vineyards and the manufacture of wine are legitimate pursuits. They must be looked upon in that light only, and the income to be derived will be in proportion to the amount of money invested. To get the net income of a vineyard, and the percentage of profits derived from the working capital invested, we will take, as an example, the reckoning already given for the value of a vineyard of thirty acres. Deducting the value of the dwelling-house and furniture, we have $14,000 as the amount of capital. This statement places the value of an acre of vineyard at $300, being one hundred per cent. advance on its original cost to the planter. However, we will not take this profit into consideration at all, but consider only the purchase price. The average yield of an acre of vineyard is four hundred gallons, and we will place the average value at only thirty cents per gallon. For thirty acres, then, we will have:

12,000 gallons of wine, at 30 cents	$3,600
600 gallons of brandy, from lees of the wine and pressings, at 75 cents, without Federal tax	450
	$4,050

Deduct expenses—		
Cultivation of vineyard, at $15 per acre	$450	
Picking grapes and making wine, at 5 cents per gallon	600	
Hauling lees to distillery and cost of distilling, at 25 cents per gallon of brandy	150	
	——	1,200
Net income		$2,850

An income of $2,850, from a working capital of $14,000, amounts to a fraction over twenty per cent. per annum.

Taking into consideration the absolute security of the pursuit; the positive, equal, and constant results from year to year, with hardly a chance of failure; the increased income as the vines grow in age, and, in consequence, the additional value acquired by the property; the pleasant occupation, and the inducement it gives for the establishment of a home and maintenance of a family — taking these all into consideration, there are few, very few, pursuits that can equal its advantages, compared to the amount of money required in its undertaking.

The question has often been asked, whether the production of wine in our State will not be overdone, and the enormously increased yearly planting of vineyards soon produce more than can be disposed of? The same question was agitated when vineyards in the Eastern States began to be planted extensively; and still they go on planting, and can not supply the demand for their products. The same doubt was expressed in the different wine-producing countries of Europe; nevertheless, the multiplication of vineyards does not suffice, compelling them to resort to adulterations, to increase the quantity of wine. The different peoples of the whole world are becoming consumers of wine; and those who are so situated as to be unable to produce it draw their supplies from those countries which are more favored by Nature.

The use of grape-wine, unlike that of alcoholic liquors, is not debasing in its results, and sometimes has a healthful effect. It stimulates the brain to activity, but never takes complete possession of it; nor does it ever create that uncontrollable craving for its possession, or suffering at its deprivation, as do alcoholic liquors.

It is a striking fact, that there is no portion of the globe where wine is made, that has not found the bulk of its consumers among its own inhabitants. No matter how deficient the quality, if it did not find admirers, it found at least drinkers. The cold, tart wines of Switzerland, the rough, acrid wines of Spain, and the harsh wines of Italy, all are used in their own country, and but little is left to ship abroad. Yet Italy is said to produce even more than France. It is probable that more than one-half of the entire amount of wine made in Europe could not bear a sea-voyage without spoiling, or even live to see its second year, with all the necessary care at home, without losing its qualities.

The total area of France is 203,736 square miles, while that of California is 188,981 square miles, or, in round numbers, nine-tenths of that of France; but in these nine-tenths we probably have, at least, four times the area where the vine will grow and bring its fruit to perfection, than is possessed by France. That country has 4,500,000 acres of vineyard, which, in round numbers, produce 900,000,000 gallons of wine annually, or an average of 200 gallons per acre. From facts in our possession it would only require one-half that number of acres of vineyard in California to yield the same amount of wine as is produced in France. Of this enormous yield of wine, hardly more than two-ninths are exported, leaving about 700,000,000 gallons to be drank by 38,000,000 French people, or eighteen gallons to each person annually. France has almost reached the utmost limit that she can spare for export; and as the demand still continues to increase in the different parts of the globe, their people will have to look elsewhere for supplies. California, by its climate, the extent of its vine-land, and the prolific qualities of its soil, is eminently qualified to supply this increased demand, and will no doubt, sooner or later, do so.

We have given statistics of the extent of the culture in France, to show our producers that there is no danger of overdoing the interest in our own State — to show them that it has not and can not be overdone in France. As to the average value of their entire crop, the lowest estimate would not set it down at less than 20 cents per gallon. Some of their wines are valued at very high prices, and bring, even in the first year, from $5 to $10 per gallon; while many others will not bring more than 10 to 15 cents per gallon. The low prices paid for the latter is due to their lack of body and deficiency in keeping quality. Such wines we have heretofore been unable to produce, as they have generally kept good in spite of ourselves; and wines like ours in France, with equally known good keeping and shipping qualities, would be worth from 30 to 35 cents per gallon. This fact must be encouraging to the wine-makers of the State, for it shows that the price, as an average throughout the State, has about reached its lowest limit.

In this series of papers we have often drawn comparisons between the imported wines and those produced in our State, and, in many cases, we may have been considered severe as against the imported wines; but we do not wish to be misunderstood, for no reflection is intended upon any of the justly renowned wines of any one of the European countries. The reputation of a fine wine — no matter in what country it be produced — is always safely guarded by the true wine-lover: he sees no nationality in a fine wine — one country may be honored in its production, but its reputation belongs to the world at large. Our remarks were aimed solely at those compound liquids sent to us, literally, as ballast for ships, and called claret — an honest name to cover an imposture. To the trade they are known as *Vin de cargaison;* and this, in the French language, conveys a grim, sarcastic double-meaning, that is not easily translated.

An analysis of the wines would probably better show the meaning than any translation. And still, we have had persons compare our pure wines with these imported fabrications; but their number has wonderfully decreased during the last few years, and they can no longer remain ignorant of the changes that have taken place, by our steady advance and constant improvement in quality. The Sauternes have been driven out of the market; then the German wines, and, in a few years, the importation to our State of *Vin de cargaison* will have become a thing of the past. No foreign wines will then be imported here, except those fine and truly grand wines, which can maintain the high position they have gained.

We have endeavored to lay before the reader the true value, actual merit, and real qualities of our wines, without the slightest exaggeration. We have claimed that they were the pure, fermented juice of the grape; were possessed of an inviting taste and pleasant bouquet; and beyond all these, that they have keeping and shipping qualities unsurpassed by any other wines in the world. Without having yet made a wine to be placed in the foremost rank of the grand wines of the world, we still claim that if each gallon of our production were rated, and the same course pursued with the entire crop of any other wine-producing country, that ours would out-rank the other. But we do not intend to stop there.

It has taken ages to discover and make known to the world the qualities of those grand wines produced from hardly more than a dozen vineyards, and we have not yet placed the name of a vineyard among this select few; but we will and the day draws nigh. Every season brings us better wines, the product of some newly discovered locality, planted with choicer varieties of the grape, and entirely different from any thing previously produced. And thus the circle will continue to narrow until California will proudly place the name of that future-discovered vineyard among those of the choicest of the earth. It will not be overshadowed by the crumbling walls of castle or monastery, whose very dampness is replete with memories of past violence and torture; nor will it require any of these auxiliaries to make its merits known. It will be the modest home of an American, surrounded by all the civilizing influences of our bright age, and with no past history but that of the peaceful, patient, and noble toils of its founder!

Notes on the Sources

"Wine-Making in California" appeared in four issues of *The Overland Monthly:* December 1871, and January, February and May 1872. The original text is as printed here with the exception of a few words added in brackets and the breaking up of long paragraphs into shorter ones.

The principal sources used in the editing and preparation of the introduction are these: Haraszthy family manuscripts, J. L. L. Warren papers, E. W. Hilgard papers, and minutes of the Board of State Viticultural Commissioners in The Bancroft Library, University of Cailfornia, Berkeley; minute books of the California Wine Association and miscellaneous papers in the library of the California Historical Society, San Francisco; copies of *The San Francisco Merchant* and its successor, the *Pacific Wine and Spirit Review,* in the San Francisco Room of the San Francisco Public Library and in The Bancroft Library; miscellaneous material in the library of the Wine Institute, San Francisco, and the California section of the California State Library, Sacramento; published reports of the Board of State Viticultural Commissioners; printed writings by Arpad Haraszthy in many publications; "The Authentic Haraszthy Story" by Paul Fredericksen, a reprint of a series of articles that appeared in the magazine *Wines & Vines* in 1947; *The Vallejos of California* by Madie Brown Emperan (San Francisco: The Gleeson Library Associates, University of San Francisco, 1968) ; and *The California Wine Industry, 1830-1895* by Vincent P. Carosso (Berkeley, California: University of California Press, 1951) .

Our thanks go to H. P. Olmo, Joan Ingalls, William Heintz and Ernest Peninou for information supplied informally, and to James D. Hart for editorial suggestions.

R. T.
C. H.

CREDITS

The portrait of Arpad Haraszthy is reproduced from the collection of the Wine Institute.

The Cherubs in the Vineyard is from The Bancroft Library, University of California, Berkeley.

The three Trade Cards and the Haraszthy bill head were loaned by the California Historical Society.

ERRATA

Page 5   Line 20—Emperan *should read* Emparan.
Page 11   Line 33 *should read* education and research.
Page 20   Line 5 *should read* done for it did not require a great quantity.
Page 33   line 10—adavntage *should read* advantage.
NOTES ON THE SOURCES   Line 10—Cailfornia *should read* California.
                        Line 24—Emperan *should read* Emparan.